A G[UIDE TO THE]
MANHATTAN PROJECT
in
TENNESSEE

THE CHAPEL-ON-THE-HILL

Built in 1943 for the Manhattan Project, this standard Army chapel served Jewish, Catholic and Protestant faiths. More than 4,000 weddings were celebrated here.

Cynthia C. Kelly
President, Atomic Heritage Foundation

Introduction by Richard Rhodes

Introduction

In 1942, when the physicist J. Robert Oppenheimer was recruiting scientists for the U.S. atomic bomb program, secrecy prevented him from revealing to them what their work would be. He told them instead that the outcome, if successful, would probably end the war—the Second World War then raging—and might, he said, end all war.

The atomic bomb did contribute to ending the Pacific War, and fear of its destructiveness has limited major war now for more than six decades. What began as a desperate effort of defense—inventing an atomic bomb before Nazi Germany got there first—became a major new force in human affairs.

The work of physics, chemistry, metallurgy and engineering that led to the new invention was accomplished in requisitioned or makeshift buildings, laboratories and factories all over the United States. Some of the largest industrial facilities in the vast project were built and operated in Tennessee, where labor was plentiful and where parallel valleys might contain a large radioactive accident if one should occur (none did).

Here were constructed huge automated refineries harnessing entirely new technologies to laboriously separate rare uranium-235 from its chemically identical cousin uranium-238, which was useless for a bomb. Tens of thousands of Americans lived and worked here in deep secrecy, not even knowing what it was they were making but believing it would help end the terrible conflict.

The scale speaks to the scale of the last world war. And now the land is peaceful.

Richard Rhodes, author, *The Making of the Atomic Bomb*

Table of Contents

Manhattan Project workers at the Y-12 Plant gate
Photo courtesy of Ed Westcott

Welcome
ATOMIC HERITAGE FOUNDATION

Legend has it that in 1900 John Hendrix, known as the "Prophet of Oak Ridge," predicted that a city would be built on Black Oak Ridge. Further, he envisioned that a huge factory in Bear Creek Valley would be built to help win the greatest war the world has ever known.

Looking back, it is uncanny how many of Hendrix's prophecies were fulfilled. In 1942, Black Oak Ridge and the neighboring ridges and valleys were selected as the first Manhattan Project site. Mammoth factories were built in Bear Creek and other valleys to bring an end to the most devastating war in history. In the six years of World War II (1939 to 1945), over 70 million lives were lost. The atomic bombs, which Oak Ridge contributed to producing, helped to bring an end to the war.

This book is a short history of the Manhattan Project in Oak Ridge. The story begins in late 1942 when the government ordered residents of five small farming communities to leave. The Army Corps of Engineers then built the fifth-largest city in Tennessee in just two-and-one-half years. Even when the population reached 75,000, Oak Ridge remained a Secret City that did not appear on any map.

Now you can visit the Secret City and drive up its winding streets past thousands of original "alphabet" houses. The newly renovated Alexander Inn was once a gathering place for visiting dignitaries. Stop at the American Museum of Science and Energy and if possible, arrange to see the major Manhattan Project facilities at the Y-12 and X-10 sites.

In late 2014, Congress designated the Manhattan Project National Historical Park with units at Oak Ridge, Los Alamos, NM and Hanford, WA. The National Park Service will preserve the stories and properties of the Manhattan Project for visitors from around the world. Enjoy!

Cynthia C. Kelly

Cynthia C. Kelly
President

Atomic Basics
THE SCIENCE BEHIND THE BOMB

Everything around us is made of **atoms**. Atoms are the smallest units that make up **elements**. At the heart of the atom is the **nucleus**, which is made up of two kinds of subatomic particles: **protons**, with a positive electric charge, and **neutrons**, with no charge. **Electrons**, with a negative charge, orbit around the nucleus. The nucleus is bound together by an incredibly strong energetic force. When the nucleus splits, nuclear energy is released.

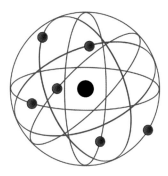

Photo courtesy of Colin M. Burtnett, Wikimedia Commons

Isotopes are different forms of the same element. They have the same number of protons and electrons but a different number of neutrons. Two naturally-occurring isotopes of uranium are **uranium-235** with 143 neutrons (235 heavy particles) and **uranium-238** with 146 neutrons (238 heavy particles).

Those extra three neutrons make all the difference. U-235 is much more unstable than U-238 and easily splits apart ("fissions") when hit by another neutron.

NUCLEAR TERMINOLOGY

Atom: building block of matter; made up of a small, dense nucleus surrounded by a cloud of negatively-charged **electrons.**

Nucleus: makes up the center of the atom; consists of a number of positively-charged **protons** and neutral **neutrons**. An atom is classified by the number of protons and neutrons in its nucleus.

Isotope: isotopes of an element possess the same number of protons in their nuclei but have different numbers of neutrons.

Fission: the process by which an atom's nucleus is split into smaller pieces; results in the release of neutrons and lots of energy.

Pile: a nuclear reactor. Coined by Enrico Fermi at the Met Lab, it was based on the first rudimentary nuclear reactor which was nothing more than a pile of uranium and graphite blocks.

The atoms of most elements—like hydrogen, oxygen, iron, or lead—are stable. Their nuclei tend to stay together rather than break apart. But uranium-235 is different. When a nucleus of this isotope is hit by a speeding neutron, it **fissions**, or splits, into two smaller nuclei plus one to three extra neutrons—and releases a lot of energy. The extra neutrons smash into more nuclei, fissioning them and releasing even more neutrons in a cascade of incredible energy.

This is called a **nuclear chain reaction.** When controlled inside a reactor, a chain reaction can use a small amount of U-235 or plutonium fuel to generate massive amounts of energy.

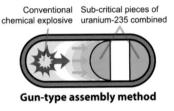

Gun-type assembly method

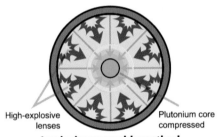

Implosion assembly method

Image courtesy of Wikimedia Commons

FAT MAN AND LITTLE BOY

In order to detonate a nuclear weapon, you need a **critical mass** of fissionable material to ensure that the neutrons released by fission will strike another nucleus and release its neutrons, producing a chain reaction. The more fissionable material you have, the greater the odds that such an event will occur.

The U.S. developed two types of atomic bombs during the Second World War using different fissionable materials--enriched uranium (U-235) and plutonium (Pu-239). Each bomb was designed to bring subcritical masses together to produce a critical mass. "**Little Boy,**" dropped on Hiroshima, was a gun-type weapon with an enriched uranium core. "**Fat Man,**" dropped on Nagasaki, was an implosion-type device with a plutonium core.

The Race for the Bomb

In a letter dated August 2, 1939, Albert Einstein warned President Franklin D. Roosevelt that Germany was probably working to produce an "extremely powerful" bomb. Einstein hoped to galvanize the United States into developing an atomic bomb before Hitler did.

Albert Einstein meets with Leo Szilard to compose his letter to FDR
Photo courtesy of the U.S. Department of Energy

In response to Einstein's letter and the urging of British prime minister Winston Churchill, President Roosevelt authorized a top-secret effort to build an atomic bomb. Organized as a military effort under the Army Corps of Engineers, scientists were recruited to work on the project from the leading universities and laboratories across the United States. In addition, scientists from Great Britain and Canada came as part of the British Mission led by Sir James Chadwick, who was awarded the Nobel Prize for his 1932 discovery of the neutron.

Dozens of refugees from Europe, many of them also Nobel Prize-winning scientists, joined the project. Together, physicists, chemists, engineers, mathematicians and other scientists designed, built and tested the world's first atomic bombs. Their drive to uncover nature's innermost secrets was combined with a sense of patriotic duty to contribute to the war effort.

Lise Meitner & Otto Hahn
Photo courtesy of the U.S. Department of Energy

LISE MEITNER: REFUGEE FROM THE NAZIS
Being Jewish, Lise Meitner was subject to the increasingly repressive anti-Semitic laws. Because so many Jewish intellectuals had already fled, in July 1938 German authorities forbade academics to emigrate. Leaving Berlin by train, Meitner barely escaped when Nazi officials inspected her expired Austrian passport at the Dutch border. She continued her study of uranium atoms in exile in Sweden. Though slim and shy, Lise was a formidable physicist and found in her work an escape from her loneliness in exile.

Research related to an atomic bomb began long before World War II. As early as 1933, Hungarian Leo Szilard conceived of the possibility of a chain reaction, the explosive force that powers an atomic bomb. In 1934, Italian physicist Enrico Fermi and his team in Rome bombarded elements with neutrons. They split uranium, but did not realize it at the time.

At the Kaiser Wilhelm Institute in Berlin, Austrian physicist Lise Meitner and German chemists Otto Hahn and Fritz Strassmann studied Fermi's data. By accident, the German chemists discovered that uranium atoms bombarded by neutrons broke into lighter particles. Otto Hahn was so disturbed by the possible military implications of his discovery that he contemplated suicide.

In December 1938, Lise Meitner correctly read the Hahn-Strassmann experiments as evidence that the uranium nuclei had been split into new particles. Meitner, along with her nephew Otto Frisch, coined the term "fission" to describe what had occurred with the uranium nucleus. They drew an analogy to a water drop dividing in two. Meitner and Frisch also theorized the potential for a chain reaction and thus, an atomic bomb.

On January 26, 1939, Danish physicist Niels Bohr announced the discoveries of Lise Meitner and her German colleagues to a physics conference at the George Washington University in Washington, DC. After learning about "atomic fission" using uranium, some attendees immediately set up an experiment to replicate the results at the nearby Carnegie Institution of Washington and elsewhere. The race for the bomb had begun.

A RACE WITH HITLER'S SCIENTISTS

Glenn Seaborg was motivated by the urgency of World War II.

"Lots of signs made us think that we were in a losing race with Hitler's scientists. We understood full well what it would have meant if Adolf Hitler had gotten the atomic bomb before the Allies did."

Interview with Academy of Achievement
September 1990

GENERAL GROVES: COOL, CONFIDENT AND DECISIVE

"My emotional graph is a straight line. I never worried. This job would never have been done if I had. I never had any doubts. Not having any doubts, I could not feel very surprised or elated by our success."

"If I can't do the job, no one man can."
Interview in Collier's *magazine*
October 1945

Photo courtesy of the U.S. Department of Energy

The project's pace quickened with the selection of hard-driving U.S. Army Corps of Engineers General Leslie R. Groves to direct the project in September 1942. Groves had been in charge of all domestic Army construction needed to mobilize for the war, including the mammoth Pentagon building.

Groves was supremely self-confident, extraordinarily decisive and an astute judge of people. Despite J. Robert Oppenheimer's past communist associations and lack of management experience, Groves recognized that Oppenheimer was critical to the success of the project and chose him as its scientific director.

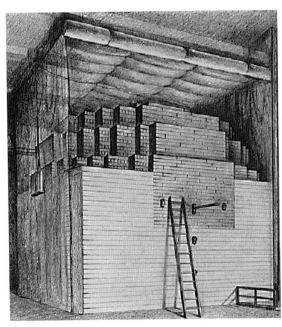

A drawing of the Chicago Pile-1
Image from AHF Archives

Enrico Fermi, Leo Szilard and other top physicists joined the Manhattan Project effort at the Metallurgical Laboratory or "Met Lab" housed at the University of Chicago.

The scientists created a "pile" of graphite blocks and uranium fuel in a squash court under the bleachers of Stagg Field. The "pile" produced the world's first controlled, self-sustaining nuclear chain reaction on December 2, 1942.

The Manhattan Project began as a small research program. At the outset, J. Robert Oppenheimer estimated that 100 scientists could do the research, design and testing at Los Alamos. But the endeavor proved to be far more complex, involving not just scientific research but a gargantuan engineering and industrial effort. Mammoth first-of-a-kind factories were built to produce the fissile material--enriched uranium and plutonium--at the core of the bombs.

Three methods of separating the isotopes of uranium were developed at Oak Ridge, TN. First, the mile-long K-25 plant used gaseous diffusion. At Y-12 plant, "Calutrons," named after the University of California's newly invented "cyclotrons," used electromagnetic forces. The S-50 plant tried a third technique, thermal separation. All three processes contributed to producing the enriched uranium for the atomic bomb used on Hiroshima. At Hanford, WA, facilities were constructed to produce plutonium that fueled the Nagasaki bomb.

Dozens of major corporations and universities were essential to the project. Niels Bohr had observed that building an atomic bomb could never be done without turning the United States into one huge factory. Bohr saw his words borne out as the nationwide project transformed America with facilities coast-to-coast.

The B Reactor at Hanford
Photo courtesy of the U.S. Department of Energy

CLINTON ENGINEER WORKS

Ridges and Valleys
GEOGRAPHY AND HISTORY

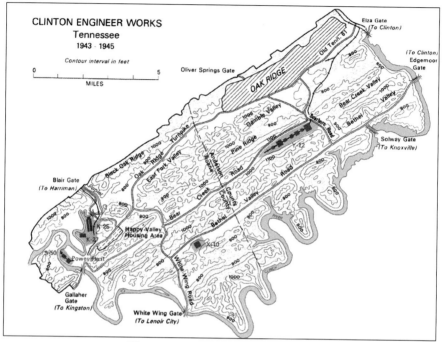

Clinton Engineer Works in Oak Ridge
Photo courtesy of The Atomic Archive

On September 19, 1942, General Leslie Groves ordered the acquisition of over 56,000 acres in East Tennessee as the principal production site for enriched uranium, one of the key ingredients of an atomic bomb. Clinton Engineer Works, named after the town of Clinton, TN, extended seventeen miles and was about seven miles wide.

The area offered many advantages. Situated along the Clinch River, the site had access to abundant water. Thanks to the Tennessee Valley Authority (TVA) and the nearby Norris, Fontana, Cherokee and Douglas dams and the Watts Bar generating stations, the site would also have access to cheap and plentiful electricity.

Five parallel ridges created natural barriers to separate the facilities. The site was close to two railroads and accessible by car. It was near enough to Knoxville, whose population of 111,000 could supply labor. The mild climate also made year-round construction possible.

George Jones Memorial Baptist Church
Photo by Brian Stansberry, Wikimedia Commons

Five farm communities dating back to the Scotch-Irish settlers of the late 1700s were nestled between the ridges. These communities were Wheat, Elza, Robertsville, Scarboro and New Hope. In Wheat, the George Jones Memorial Baptist Church stands as the only structure left over from the Wheat community before the Manhattan Project. Residents commemorate the history with annual "homecomings" held at the church.

Three thousand area residents were ordered to vacate their family homes by February 1943. Some of the residents took the eviction especially hard. However, most residents responded positively to the U.S. government's appeal that the land was crucial to win the war. Many took advantage of well-paid jobs and improved their lives.

FROM FARMS TO FACTORIES

"We lived in the East Fork valley [now Robertsville Road in Oak Ridge] for many generations. My grandfather had two brothers and two sisters who lived there so we were all nicely settled. My great grandparents lived on the hill…The first official [eviction] notice came in January 1943…It was very rough going through this but my parents and my grandparents all took jobs on the project.

"My mother and grandmother had never worked outside the house. Believe it or not, they took jobs, too, which meant they could pursue their hobbies at home and have a check coming in every month.

"My mother was a chaufferette. She drove the bigwigs around so she was connected with people who were in a position to hire me. Finally one of the men asked her, "Has she had chemistry?" It took just a few days for me to pass the Q [security] clearance and I went to work at the analytical lab at Y-12."
~Reba Justice Holmberg, AHF oral history, September 22, 2005

Columbia University
NEW YORK, NY

Much of the work done on uranium enrichment in Oak Ridge, TN began in New York, NY. At Columbia University, Dr. Harold Urey and Dr. John Dunning attempted to develop the gaseous diffusion method at the Substitute Alloy Materials (SAM) laboratory, the code name for the top-secret nuclear laboratory.

The gaseous diffusion technique separated the lighter isotopes of U-235 from the heavier, more common U-238 by turning uranium metal into a gas. The gas was pumped through a porous barrier material that allowed the lighter U-235 to pass through more quickly than the heavier U-238.

Harold Urey
Photo courtesy of Columbia University

DONALD TRAUGER: WORKING IN MANHATTAN

Photo courtesy of the Oak Ridger

"In late summer 1943, I began work at Columbia University's Pupin Laboratory on the gaseous diffusion separation process. My work was to develop a means for separating the isotopes of uranium, testing the barrier to see whether or not the pores were fine enough, uniform enough, and whether it would withstand the rigors of the operation of the plant.

"Dr. [Eugene] Booth took a great interest in my testing facilities, particularly at the Nash building, because it was so key to the future of the project. He would come to visit my laboratory every Saturday afternoon. We were working 7 days a week and long days. It was really a privilege and a wonderful learning experience."

~Donald B. Trauger, AHF oral history, September 22, 2005

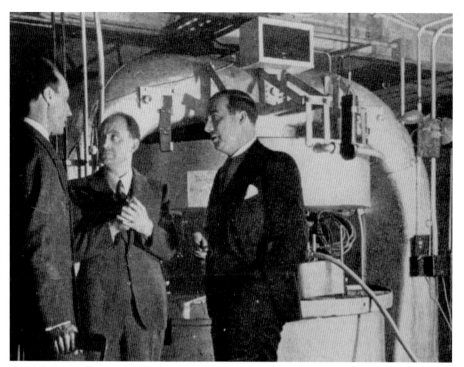

John Dunning, Enrico Fermi, and Dana P. Mitchell with the Columbia cyclotron
Photo courtesy of the AIP Emilio Segrè Visual Archives

Due to the minute difference in mass between the uranium isotopes, a single diffusion step would separate only a tiny fraction of the two isotopes. The gas had to be pumped through a long series, or cascade, of the equipment. By the time it reached the end, the percent of U-235 in the product would have increased as the heavier U-238 isotopes would more often fail to pass through the barrier material.

Having designed the method with George Pegram and Eugene Booth, Dunning was confident that the gaseous diffusion method would work for large-scale production. Despite numerous unsolved technical issues, Dunning's unwavering optimism convinced General Groves to construct a mile-long plant at Oak Ridge.

To design the plant, M. W. Kellogg Company, an engineering giant, created the Kellex Corporation. With offices in the Woolworth building in Manhattan, Percival "Dobie" Keith directed the Kellex work on the K-25 gaseous diffusion plant. The Nash Garage building housed a pilot plant built by Columbia to produce the barrier material. Hundreds worked first in Manhattan and then in Oak Ridge on the actual K-25 gaseous diffusion plant.

Clinton Engineer Works

General Leslie Groves
Photo courtesy of the U.S. Department of Energy

The Manhattan Engineer District (MED or "Manhattan Project ") was run by the Army Corps of Engineers. Expert at managing huge construction projects, the Corps was the logical choice to organize and direct the ambitious scientific and industrial undertaking.

The name Manhattan Engineer District reflects the fact that its first headquarters were in downtown Manhattan. The Clinton Engineer Works was named after the town of Clinton, TN, the seat of Anderson County where the top-secret production site was located. In August 1943, MED's headquarters were moved to the Tennessee site.

General Leslie Groves was a man of extraordinary ability and capacity to get things done. Extremely decisive, Groves gave himself one hour

DETERMINED TO WIN

"He was very, very competitive. He played games not to play games, but to win. In wrestling, he liked to rub people's nose in the mat, climb on top of them. You didn't want to play a game with him, because you were probably going to lose. If you didn't, he'd come back until he beat you...He was after winning."

~Richard H. Groves (son), AHF oral history, December 5, 2007

or less to make a decision. The second day after taking command, on September 19, 1942, Groves approved acquiring the farmland in East Tennessee to be the top-secret site for enriched uranium production.

Groves recruited America's top corporations, appealing to the patriotism of executives at DuPont, M.W. Kellogg, Union Carbide, Tennessee Eastman, General Electric, Westinghouse, Stone and Webster and dozens of other firms. A masterful bureaucrat, Groves obtained a AAA priority for procurement and a virtual blank check.

Groves' overriding concern in managing the project was secrecy. Billboards warned workers not to discuss their jobs with anyone except their supervisor. Groves created separate intelligence and surveillance organizations reporting directly to him. As the only person who knew about the entire project, Groves wielded great power.

A billboard from Oak Ridge
Photo courtesy of the U.S. Department of Energy

19

Colonel Kenneth Nichols

Groves appointed 34-year-old Colonel Kenneth D. Nichols as his second in command. Nichols' title was district engineer for the Manhattan Engineer District (MED). Using the Andrew Jackson Hotel in Knoxville as his base, Nichols began working on the production site in East Tennessee.

First, Nichols had a road built between Knoxville and Oak Ridge. Next, he hired Skidmore, Owings and Merrill (SOM), a New York architectural and engineering firm, to design a town for 30,000 people from scratch. SOM was given some aerial photographs and a few topographical maps but no information about its secret location.

Once the Army approved their initial plan, the entire SOM office of 400 people moved to Tennessee. The team produced one of the fastest and most skillful jobs of town planning ever seen. Following the contours of Black Oak Ridge, the town was a narrow strip less than one mile wide and six miles long.

SOM designed 3,000 prefabricated houses made from "cemesto," a cement-asbestos board. The houses were shipped from a factory in Indiana complete with walls, floors, room partitions, interior wiring, plumbing and furniture. The homes were quickly installed along streets that followed the natural contours of the hills. Built with wartime urgency, they have graced Oak Ridge for nearly seven decades.

OAK RIDGE OUTLASTS EXPECTATIONS

Oak Ridge was a city without a past, and it was not designed to have much of a future. We tried to design only for the duration of the war, in order to conserve money, materials, and labor...The foundations laid were more lasting than we expected...After spending three exciting years planning, constructing, and living in Oak Ridge, I am pleased that this once temporary town has fixed its place, permamently, in the history and future of those towns that make up Tennessee.

~Kenneth D. Nichols, These Are Our Voices, *pages 116-117*

Isotope Separation

Separating the two isotopes of uranium was a great challenge. However, through collaboration and hard work, engineers and scientists were able to achieve this monumental task.

In nature, over 99 percent of uranium is made of the isotope U-238, which is very stable. Less than one percent is U-235, which is fissile.

The two atoms are chemically identical and so close in weight that they are like two basketballs, only one with a nickel taped to it. Not knowing what technique would work, three possible separation methods were pursued during the Manhattan Project years:

Electromagnetic separation using calutrons designed by the Univerity of California at Berkeley (used for the Y-12 plant starting in January 1944),

Gaseous diffusion forcing uranium hexafluoride gas through membranes with microscopic pores (used for the K-25 plant starting in January 1945), and

Thermal diffusion using temperature differences to separate the two isotopes (used for the S-50 plant starting in October 1944).

Uranium-238 has three extra neutrons and is slightly heavier. **Uranium-235** is lighter and more active.

In nature, there are 140 atoms of U-238 for every atom of U-235. The Manhattan Project produced over 80% enriched uranium U-235.

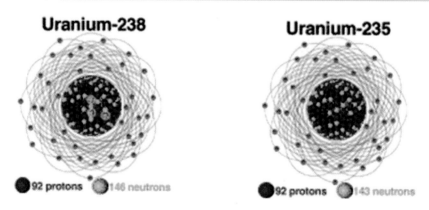

Common uranium isotopes
Image courtesy of Silex.com

SED
SPECIAL ENGINEER DETACHMENT

Oak Ridge SED group in uniform

In 1943, the Manhattan Engineer District could not find enough technically trained people to work at the various plants and laboratories involved in the atomic bomb project around the country. On May 22, 1943, the Special Engineer Detachment (SED) was created to help fill the need.

UNDERCOVER AGENTS AT Y-12

"I was studying chemistry in the Army Specialized Training Program at Penn State. One Saturday morning, the Army took a hundred of us out for a test...They picked out those who had some college or training and sent us to Oak Ridge....We ended up in the Farragut Hotel in Knoxville and the first thing the captain said, "Send home for your civilian clothes." [The Y-12 plant just had a shutdown that they feared was caused by sabotage.] We had to keep an eye on vulnerable spots in the process that might be open to sabotage. They couldn't afford any more shutdowns."

~Raymond Stein, AHF oral history, June 2007

Harold "Hal" Hoover was another of the 12 or so SEDers who worked in counterintelligence at Y-12. Hal served as a "filter foreman."

FROM VERMONT TO OAK RIDGE

"I came from a little town in Vermont called Richford, right on the Canadian line, and went to Dartmouth College. Graduating with a degree in chemistry in 1943, I went to work for Hooker Electrochemical in Niagara Falls. There we were making the organic materials used as a coolant in the first K-25 plant.

"We finished up and I got drafted. I figured I was on my way to Japan but then they put me on a train and I wound up in Oak Ridge. And I've been here ever since. I never studied anything about how to operate a plant. But that's what I wound up helping to do. And I had a lot of fun doing it."

~Robert Dyer, AHF oral history, June 2005

The first 343 SEDers arrived in Oak Ridge on July 19, 1943. Some, like Lawrence S. O'Rourke and William E. Tewes, first worked at the Substitute Alloy Materials (SAM) laboratory at Columbia University or other sites in New York City developing the gaseous diffusion process before coming to Oak Ridge.

The SED came from 300 different universities and 47 states. The peak enrollment at Oak Ridge was 1,257 in September 1945. The average SED's Army General Classification Test Score was 133, perhaps the highest in the Army.

Col. Kenneth D. Nichols praised the SED for its specialized talents and contributions. They were the "cream of the crop" of the U. S. Army and provided essential skills and manpower. At a ceremony in December 2010 honoring SED members in Oak Ridge, veteran Bill Wilcox praised them as the "unsung heroes" of the Manhattan Project.

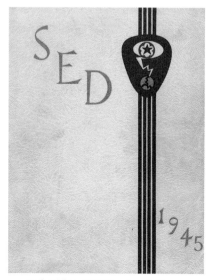

Oak Ridge SED Yearbook Cover

Knoxville
THE GATEWAY OF OAK RIDGE

Car stuck in the mud of Oak Ridge, TN
Photo courtesy of Ed Westcott

Part of Oak Ridge's appeal to Manhattan Project planners was nearby Knoxville with its population of 111,000. However, the top-secret project was not warmly welcomed in Knoxville, arousing both suspicion and resentment. Many saw the people flooding into East Tennessee from all over the country—and the world—as "furriners" who could not be questioned. In a time of austerity and rationing, others resented Oak Ridge residents arriving with unlimited ration stamps and fistfuls of cash.

Oak Ridgers who ventured into Knoxville were easy to spot. The quickly constructed secret city was blanketed in a thick layer of mud. As a result, its residents' muddy shoes were a dead giveaway as to their origin.

One young boy recalled accompanying his father, a butcher, to make a delivery in Oak Ridge. They handed the meat over at the gate, where an armed guard inspected it and placed it in a waiting army truck. No explanation was given. "Incidents like that gave Oak Ridge and its people an aura of science fiction."

However grudgingly, Knoxville residents did see the positive side of Oak Ridge's development. Business was stronger, as these residents brought money to spend. One Knoxville woman recalled, "The important impact that Oak Ridge had on Knoxville for me was the availability of men." Knoxville's male population had been severely depleted by the war overseas. Now, thousands of young, unmarried men were available.

After the bomb was dropped on Hiroshima on August 6, 1945 and Oak Ridge's secret mission was revealed, tensions between Oak Ridge and Knoxville more or less evaporated. East Tennessee residents were proud their area had such a vital role in the war effort and finally understood why Oak Ridgers had such special treatment during the war.

On August 7, 1945, a porter on the Southern Railroad proudly announced to his passengers, "You are now entering Knoxville, the gateway to Oak Ridge."

KNOXVILLE: CITY OF LOVE & DESTINY
Manhattan Project veteran Ted Rockwell shares his early memories.

Mary Compton
Photo courtesy of Ted Rockwell

Soon after Pearl Harbor with her new high school diploma, Mary Compton was offered a war job with TVA. In March 1942, she flew into Knoxville and stayed at the YWCA until she got a room at a boarding house. When the government halted TVA construction work, in early 1944 Mary moved to Oak Ridge to work for Tennessee Eastman. At first, Mary continued her studies in Knoxville while working at the Y-12 plant. After finishing the first semester, she dropped out as the commute was too taxing.

Meanwhile, Ted Rockwell, a recent 20-year-old graduate from Princeton, flew into Knoxville in December 1943 to interview for a job. Soon enough, Rockwell's path crossed Mary's and it was love at first sight. As Rockwell recalled: "After that, it was just a matter of time before we were married in the Chapel on the Hill."

Security and Secrecy
ESPIONAGE AT OAK RIDGE

General Leslie R. Groves was obsessed with secrecy and took security measures to unprecedented heights. The Manhattan Project sites had to be located in remote and sparsely settled areas. In the early 1940s, there were only a few farming communities nestled in the ridges and valleys that became the Clinton Engineer Works (CEW).

Around the CEW site, multiple security checkpoints were guarded by military police twenty-four hours a day, seven days a week. In addition, tall barbed-wire fencing surrounded the perimeter, preventing intruders from gaining unwanted access to key buildings and deterring any employee from sneaking out with classified documents or materials.

Each worker at the Manhattan Project underwent a rigorous background check conducted by the FBI. Every employee that worked at one of the Manhattan Project sites had a security badge that displayed his or her picture, job position, and level of clearance. In addition, all mail coming in and going out was carefully censored.

Military Police inspect a car trunk at Elza Gate at Oak Ridge
Photo courtesy of Currents of Change

George Koval
SOVIET SPY

Soviet spies infiltrated the Manhattan Project and passed key information to the USSR. George Koval (right) spied for the Soviets while working at Oak Ridge and Dayton, OH.

Born in 1913 in Sioux City, Iowa to Russian immigrants, Koval and his parents moved back to Russia in 1932. There he studied chemical engineering. In 1939, the Soviet secret police recruited him as a spy and instructed him to return to America. Koval was drafted into the Army and in August 1944 was selected for the Army's Special Engineer Detachment (SED).

Assigned to Oak Ridge, Koval became a Health Physics officer. According to FBI files, he had top-secret clearance. With access to Oak Ridge's key facilities, Koval provided information about them to the Soviets. In June 1945, Koval was transferred to Dayton, OH where the polonium-based "initiator" for the implosion bomb was being developed. Koval also passed important information about this work. In 1948, he left the United States for Europe and possibly went to Russia.

Koval was never accused of espionage. However, in 2007 Russian President Putin posthumously awarded Koval with the Hero of Russia Medal for his contributions to the Russian atomic project.

AN UNSUSPECTED SPY

"I met George Koval in Dayton. He was an instrument technician there, maintaining instruments that I had worked on to improve from pre-war designs. He was a very nice guy. We became friends. He was an excellent technician, knew his job very well, and was very friendly. As a health physicist, he was able to gain access to many key sites at Oak Ridge and Dayton. Of course, I had no idea he was a spy. The amazing thing is that he wasn't detected and got away with it."
~James A. Schoke (pictured), AHF oral history, November 2014

Control room panels with operator at the Y-12 Plant
Photo courtesy of Ed Westcott

PRODUCTION PLANTS

Mannequins at the X-10 Graphite Reactor

The X-10 Graphite Reactor was the first reactor built after the successful experimental "Chicago Pile-I" at the University of Chicago. On December 2, 1942, using a lattice of graphite blocks and uranium rods, Enrico Fermi proved that a nuclear chain reaction could be controlled. Scientists knew that it would only be a matter of time before the energy of the atom could be harnessed for a bomb.

The next step was to build a reactor to produce plutonium, a potential ingredient for an atomic weapon. Like enriched uranium, plutonium is unstable. A man-made element, plutonium was discovered by Glenn Seaborg and colleagues at the University of California at Berkeley in late 1940.

The X-10 Graphite Reactor or "Clinton Pile" was a pilot plant for the full-scale plutonium production reactors that were being built at Hanford. DuPont was hired to work with the University of Chicago to design and build both the Oak Ridge and Hanford reactors.

Racing against time, DuPont decided to use air to cool the pilot reactor. Just ten months after construction began, the X-10 reactor went critical on November 4, 1943. Workers loaded uranium-metal slugs into the 1,248 channels of the reactor, a twenty-four foot graphite cube. Once irradiated in the reactor core, the slugs dropped into a pool of water. After the slugs had lost some radioactivity, the plutonium was extracted from the slugs in a separations plant.

While X-10 was still under construction, DuPont decided that water should be used as a coolant for the Hanford reactors. While X-10 was not an exact prototype for the Hanford reactors, it did produce valuable samples of plutonium for the scientists at Los Alamos designing the bombs. In total, the X-10 graphite reactor cost $27 million to build and operate during the war years and employed 1,513 workers.

In 1946, X-10 began producing peacetime radioisotopes for use in industry, agriculture, medicine and research. The pile was permanently shut down in 1963 and designated a National Historic Landmark in 1966 and a National Historic Chemical Landmark in 2008. The reactor has also been recently renovated and is often included in tours provided by Oak Ridge National Laboratory (ORNL) to visitors.

A TRIBUTE TO ALVIN WEINBERG

Alvin Weinberg came to the University of Chicago in 1939. Working with Enrico Fermi, he helped develop the Chicago Pile-I. After moving to Oak Ridge in 1945, he worked on the X-10 Graphite Reactor.

Weinberg was director of the Oak Ridge National Laboratory (1955 to 1973) and later director of the Office of Energy Research and Development under President Richard Nixon. He believed in the potential of "big science" and envisioned that cheap sustainable nuclear power could transform the third world.

Weinberg was beloved by the community. Noting the difference between Chicago and Oak Ridge, Weinberg reportedly said, "When piles go critical in Chicago, we celebrate with wine. When piles go critical in Tennessee, we celebrate with Jack Daniel's."

~Sam Beall, Tribute to Alvin M. Weinberg

Y-12
ELECTROMAGNETIC SEPARATION PLANT

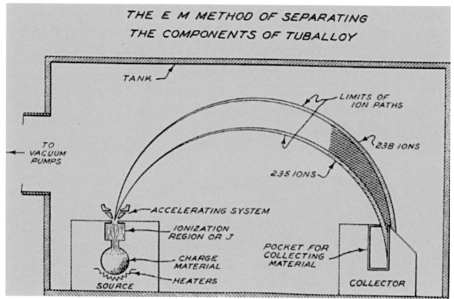

Electromagnetic method of separating uranium isotopes
Image courtesy of Wikimedia Commons

The electromagnetic separation method was the most developed of the potential ways to produce fissile material at the start of the Manhattan Project. Ernest O. Lawrence, working at the University of California-Berkeley, determined that when an electrically-charged atom was placed in a magnetic field, it would trace a circular path with a radius determined by the atom's mass. U-235 was lighter than U-238 and could be isolated by placing a collecting pocket in its path.

The massive Y-12 plant at Oak Ridge was designed to carry out on a large scale what Lawrence had successfully done in his Berkeley lab. While the machines in California were called cyclotrons, at Y-12 they were dubbed "calutrons" from *CALifornia University cycloTRONs*. Ground was broken for the Tennessee facility on February 18, 1943.

There were 1,152 calutrons at Y-12. The beta calutrons resembled the capital letter D and were arranged in giant ellipses called "racetracks", while the alpha calutrons were rectangular. Because of wartime shortage of copper, the huge magnetic coils had to be wound with 14,700 tons of silver obtained from the U.S. Treasury.

Wartime labor shortages forced Tennessee Eastman Corporation to recruit young women, mostly recent high school graduates and farm girls. Even though they were not told what they were producing, the women were very adept at the controls. They worked in cubicles and were called "cubicle girls" (back then the term "calutron" was secret).

Known now as the "calutron girls," the women proved in a week-long test to have an excellent feel for how to adjust the knobs to optimize production. Their performance was dramatically better than the male Ph.D. physicists who were constantly fiddling with the controls.

Despite being plagued by troubles, the Y-12 plant eventually produced the enriched uranium for the first atomic bomb. But the calutrons required an exorbitant amount of energy and over 22,000 employees. In December 1946, all of the Y-12 calutrons were shut down, except for the 36 calutrons in the Beta 3 building and the pilot units in Building 9731.

Starting in 1959, the Beta 3 calutrons were used to produce over 200 stable isotopes used for cancer treatment, medical diagnostics, nonproliferation, and other applications. In 1998, production was shut down but the control room and other portions of the facility remain as they were in 1945.

A TRIBUTE TO WILLIAM J. "BILL" WILCOX

Bill Wilcox was a life-long resident of Oak Ridge, a Manhattan Project veteran, and Oak Ridge's city historian. After graduating from Washington and Lee University in 1943, he began work in the Secret City as a government chemist and worked in high level posts in the Y-12 plant.

Photo courtesy of Oak Ridger

Bill remained heavily involved in preserving the Manhattan Project heritage of Oak Ridge until his death in 2013. He was the catalyst for the Secret City Commemorative Walk and founded the Partnership for K-25 Preservation (PKP). He and his wife Jeanie met during the Manhattan Project and raised their family in Oak Ridge. The new park is a fitting tribute to Bill, who worked hard to preserve Oak Ridge's history.

K-25
GASEOUS DIFFUSION PLANT

The original K-25 Plant
Photo courtesy of Wikimedia Commons

The K-25 plant was an enormously ambitious and risky undertaking. A mile-long, U-shaped building, the K-25 plant was the world's largest roofed building at the time. British scientists working on the "tube alloy," code for the atomic bomb project, first advocated the gaseous diffusion method in March 1941. Because of the Nazi bombing of England, any production plants had to be located elsewhere.

Columbia University's John R. Dunning and Eugene Booth began working in 1941 on the gaseous diffusion process. The goal was to separate the isotopes of U-235 from U-238. Uranium metal was converted into uranium hexaflouride gas and pumped through a barrier material that had millions of microscopic holes.

Developing an effective barrier material was the greatest challenge. Columbia University's SAM Labs, Kellex, and Union Carbide all pursued major programs addressing this very difficult problem, and all contributed to its eventual solution. With immense time pressures, General Groves ordered construction to begin and the plant was one-third complete before a solution was found.

TRANSLATING "K-25"

When General Groves contracted M. W. Kellogg Company to design the top-secret plant, Kellogg created the Kellex Corporation. The plant site was named "K-25" with "K" for Kellex and "25" for "U-235." "25" was a common designation for U-235 during the project.

K-25 cost $512 million to build, or $6.5 billion in 2010 dollars. The mile-long, U-shaped plant covered forty-four acres, was four stories high and up to 400 feet wide. Engineers developed special coatings for the hundreds of miles of pipes and equipment to withstand the corrosive uranium hexaflouride gas that would pass through the plant's 3,000 repetitive diffusion stages (together making up a cascade).

The entire process was hermetically sealed like a thermos bottle, as any moisture could cause a violent reaction with the uranium hexafluoride. Even minute pinhole leaks and contamination from fingerprints were major concerns. With a special leak detector, every component was thoroughly inspected before and after it was installed.

The K-25 plant was the first large-scale fully automated factory in history. Because of the complexity and size of the plant, 9,000 employees worked in three shifts to monitor its operations.

The K-25 plant was more reliable and efficient than anyone predicted. After the war, the K-25 was expanded with the K-27, K-29, K-31 and K-33 plants built as additional stages of the process. The plants produced the majority of the U-235 for the Cold War arsenal.

Until 1985, K-25 produced fuel for civilian nuclear power reactors around the world. In addition, K-25 developed a commercially competitive gas centrifuge technology. K-25's innovative technologies served the nation in World War II and the Cold War with great distinction. In 2013, the Department of Energy finished demolishing the historic facility.

K-25 Demolition
Photo courtesy of the U.S. Department of Energy

The S-50 Plant Process Building
Photo courtesy of the U.S. Department of Energy

With both the K-25 and Y-12 plants suffering setbacks in the spring of 1944, Oppenheimer urged Groves to approve the construction of a thermal diffusion plant. The U.S. Navy had researched this method for three years and was already building a pilot plant of 100 columns in Philadelphia. After reviewing Oppenheimer's suggestions, Groves decided in late June 1944 to approve construction for what would become the S-50 Thermal Diffusion Plant.

Closely patterned on the Navy pilot plant in Philadelphia, the S-50 plant consisted of 2,142 uniform columns, each 48 feet high. Manufacturing this plant to exacting specifications within 90 days would be no small feat. Indeed, 21 firms turned down the assignment before the H. K. Ferguson Company, an engineering firm in Cleveland, accepted the challenge.

The construction of the plant demanded a high level of precision. It required nearly perfectly round columns with a uranium hexafluoride layer spacing of only 0.010 inches (3 sheets of paper) thick! In order to meet the nearly impossible deadline, operators, electricians and welders scrambled to complete the project and even used passenger trains to transport construction materials. In the end, the contractors beat the deadline and completed the S-50 plant in just 69 days.

The theory behind investing in a third plant was that the enrichment process might work best if the three plants were used in a series. In practice, this proved to be correct. The uranium product was slightly enriched at S-50 (one to two percent U-235) and this was fed into the K-25 plant. The gaseous diffusion process raised the enrichment to about 20 percent. This was fed into the Y-12 plant for the final enrichment cycle. Through this serial approach, the first atomic bomb received its enriched uranium.

The S-50 production plant required an enormous amount of energy and was shut down in 1946. The K-25 plant was most effective.

PROFILE: PHILIP H. ABELSON

Phil Abelson studied physics at University of California at Berkeley under E. O. Lawrence and knew many of the Manhattan Project physicists. Hired by the U.S. Navy, Abelson developed the thermal diffusion process for the Navy's possible use for nuclear-powered submarines. Knowing the difficulties that Oak Ridge plants were experiencing, Abelson wrote a memo to Edward Teller about the thermal diffusion process. Teller shared it with Oppenheimer, who later used it as a means to convince Groves to reverse his earlier decision to not pursue thermal diffusion methods.

Abelson recalls the excitement that he felt after he was asked to bring his work to Oak Ridge:

"I got word one day that I was to go to the Warner Theater and go to the balcony at 8 o'clock. I would be approached by a man who would identify himself and I was to have a summary of the status of the liquid thermal diffusion project. So I went and I met with [Admiral William S.] "Deak" Parsons... Shortly thereafter the order of General Groves was to make a Chinese copy of what they have at Philadelphia Navy Yard."

Innovations
OAK RIDGE NATIONAL LABORATORY

The Titan supercomputer at ORNL, one of the fastest supercomputers in the world
Photo courtesy of ORNL

Clinton Laboratories' future was uncertain after the bombs were dropped on Japan. In late 1944, Hungarian physicist Eugene Wigner sketched a plan for a post-war laboratory devoted to nuclear research and reactor technology. The transition, however, wasn't so simple.

According to the Oak Ridge National Laboratory's 50-year retrospective published in 1992, "Change was the watchword in the tumultuous postwar period, as one unexpected event followed another." In 1947, the brand-new civilian Atomic Energy Commission (AEC) replaced the Army Corps of Engineers to manage the formerly top-secret nuclear production sites and laboratories.

In 1948, the laboratory was renamed the Oak Ridge National Laboratory (ORNL) as part of the new national laboratory system to support "Big Science" that required expensive equipment. Oak Ridge was

ORNL INNOVATIONS IN OUR HOMES
Oak Ridge innovations are important to our lives. Some daily uses of ORNL innovations across U.S. homes include:
- Use of DNA research to understand the causes of cancer
- Radiation detectors and dosimeters
- Mass spectrometry techniques to detect explosives
- More efficient appliances, such as refrigerators
- Better joint implants and surgical aneurysm clips
- Flu vaccines and other relevant medicines
- Touch screen computer technology

~Oak Ridge Convention and Visitors' Bureau

The Spallation Neutron Source: the most intense pulsed neutron beams in the world
Photo courtesy of ORNL

given a broad mandate for fundamental scientific research. The late 1940s were especially prolific as the laboratory explored new issues ranging from the genetic effects of prolonged exposure to radiation to ecological issues such as the natural movement of nutrients. With impetus from Admiral Hyman Rickover, ORNL established the Oak Ridge School of Reactor Technology that turned out 100 graduates a year who became leaders in the new field of nuclear power. ORNL also began to design the first pressurized water reactor. As a result, the first commercial power plant in the U.S. was operational in 1958 at Shippingport, PA. The same year, the *Nautilus*, the first nuclear submarine, sailed under the North Pole.

In 1946, Oak Ridge pioneered cancer treatment with radioisotopes produced by the X-10 Graphite Reactor. The use of radioisotopes was expanded rapidly with numerous applications in industry, agriculture, and medical imaging and treatment.

Today, ORNL conducts research in a diverse number of fields including neutron science, biological systems, energy, advanced materials, national security, supercomputing, and chemical sciences. For example, since 2006 the Spallation Neutron Source facility has enabled researchers from all over the world to study the science of materials. This work is essential to emerging technologies in energy, telecommunications, manufacturing, transportation, information technology, biotechnology, and health. Spawned by the Manhattan Project, the traditions of scientific excellence and innovation continue.

Children at Oak Ridge
Photo courtesy of Ed Westcott

LIFE IN THE SECRET CITY

Alphabet Houses

"A" house   "B" house

The town site was in the northeast corner of the reservation, a strip less than one mile wide and six miles long with hilly terrain descending from the Black Oak Ridge in the north. Town planners were originally to provide housing for an estimated 30,000 people, but by 1945, the population had reached 75,000.

Architectural firm Skidmore, Owings & Merrill (SOM) envisioned pleasant neighborhood communities with libraries, schools and shopping centers. However, wartime constraints limited the availability of labor and materials. Rather than performing time-consuming grading, houses were adjusted to fit the contours of the land. Most of Oak Ridge's kitchens faced the street to minimize the length of plumbing and utility lines.

Materials were in short supply, so the first houses were built of prefabricated panels of cement and asbestos, or "cemesto," board. They were known as "alphabet houses" because each of the handful of home designs was assigned a letter of the alphabet. There were small, two-bedroom "A" houses, "C" houses with extra bedrooms, "D" houses with a dining room, and so forth for a total of 3,000 cemesto-type homes.

Later, thousands of prefabricated houses were sent to Oak Ridge in sections complete with walls, floors, room partitions, plumbing and wiring. Workers turned over 30 or 40 houses to occupants each day. The Roane-Anderson Company administered all housing facilities.

Alphabet Houses in Oak Ridge, TN.
Photo courtesy of Werner News Agency, Knoxville, TN

In addition to the alphabet houses, college-style dormitories housed single professionals. Women were strictly forbidden in the male dorms. Some married women who were waiting for housing were arrested for sneaking into their husbands' dormitory rooms.

In addition to dormitories, there were family apartments, prefab "flat-tops" and "victory cottages," trailers and hutments. Hutments were tiny, sixteen-foot-square buildings constructed out of thin plywood and nailed to two-by-two studs. Thirty-two thousand of Oak Ridge's workers, including most of the African-Americans, lived in hutments.

Problems accommodating 75,000 people in less than three years were inevitable. Cramped living conditions, constant construction and long lines were the norm. But most people recognized life in Oak Ridge was far preferable to fighting the Nazis in Europe or the Japanese in the Pacific and learned to "make do."

HOUSING BY NUMBER
"The housing was controlled by the Army. You could not just go in and say, 'I want an A house, or a B house or a C house.' You put your name on the list for housing, and it was done according to the size family you had."

~Colleen Black, AHF oral history, September 21, 2005

Making Do
WARTIME HARDSHIPS

YES, WE KNOW IT'S MUDDY...

"You think prices are too high in the grocery store—coal has not been delivered—it takes six days to get your laundry—the grocer runs out of butter and milk—your house leaks—everyone is not courteous—you had to move from your dorm—you can't eat a late snack—it takes too long to get your passes—the beer ran out—the telephones are always busy."

~*Town Manager R. R. O'Meara*, The Oak Ridge Journal (1943)

The list of complaints was long. There were shortages of meat, sugar and nylon. Laundry had to be done by hand on a scrub board or sent out to one of the unreliable laundries (one of which was nicknamed "the shredder" for its treatment of clothes). Oak Ridgers had to stand in line for everything from food to recreation to medical treatment. Town Manager R. R. O'Meara was tasked with administering the town and fixing what problems he could as they arose.

Despite the frustrations of living in wartime, Oak Ridge residents developed ways to unwind and temporarily forget the hardships.

Roller Skating at Oak Ridge
Photo courtesy of Ed Westcott

44

Children at Oak Ridge Library
Photo courtesy of Ed Westcott

The Recreation and Welfare Association monitored the town's theaters, bowling alleys, recreation halls and taverns. The Association also organized athletic pursuits such as baseball, boxing and wrestling, social activities such as chess matches and dances, arts and crafts, music and drama.

Cooking was another challenge. The women of Oak Ridge faced the same limitations imposed by rationing as their counterparts across the nation. They had to make do with what was available and make the best of their circumstances.

The thrifty spirit and good nature of Oak Ridgers helped alleviate tensions. Children, too, coped through various activities organized by the community, including movie nights, sports events, book readings, and other recreational activities.

RIDIN' HIGH IN OAK RIDGE

Some residents alleviated wartime tension in other ways. When Ginny and Gus Smith moved to Oak Ridge, they were informed liquor was strictly prohibited on the reservation. However, they soon heard that alcohol could be purchased in nearby Oakdale.

The Smiths would tuck their illicit purchase underneath the bassinet of their baby Kathie, who would accompany them to Oakdale in the backseat. The couple would drive until Kathie fell asleep, then approach the security guard at Oak Ridge's gate.

The guard would search their car, but when he looked at the bassinet that was "ridin' high" in the backseat, the couple implored, "Please don't disturb our baby. We just got her to sleep." The guard would wave them through the gate.

Women
IN OAK RIDGE

"Calutron" Girl
Photo courtesy of Ed Westcott

Images of Oak Ridge's women workers are some of the most iconic of the Manhattan Project. The women worked as members of the Women's Army Corps (WACs) while others were recruited by companies hired to operate the mammoth plants.

The Tennessee Eastman Corporation hired mainly women to work on the "calutrons" at the Y-12 site. Others were employed by Union Carbide to operate the K-25 plant. Depending upon their education and training, women worked as scientists, technicians, engineers, nurses, secretaries or office staff. For many women, the opportunity for employment at Oak Ridge was a significant step up the social and economic ladder.

As caretakers and providers, the schedules for women with families at Oak Ridge were very full. With long lines at stores, taking care of everyday necessities significantly added extra hours to a woman's day.

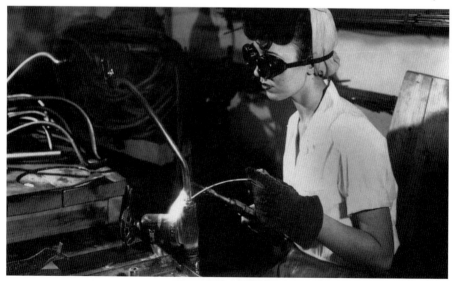

Woman K-25 welder
Photo courtesy of Ed Westcott

Oak Ridge Women at the Grocery Store
Photo courtesy of Ed Westcott

Generally, Oak Ridge housing policy was sex-biased. Women were not eligible to register for a place to live on their own. Without a spouse to sign on for a house, single women were housed in dormitory-style buildings where they would share amenities with other women. The same rule would apply to married women who were unaccompanied by their husbands at the registration offices.

Most women were young, either just out of high school or college and away from home for the first time. It was an exciting time in their lives. Even if the product of their work was top-secret, everyone understood what they were doing was important. Their job was to bring an end to the war and let their loved ones, relatives and friends fighting overseas come home. That's all they needed to know.

GREAT LIFE FOR A SINGLE PERSON

"It was fun from even the very beginning. Everybody there was in the same boat I was. We were all new, we'd all come from somewhere else. We had a good time. It was a great life for single people in Oak Ridge."

~Rosemary Lane (Oak Ridge Nurse), AHF oral history, July 17, 2011

African Americans
IN OAK RIDGE

Wheat Community African Burial Ground Monument
Photo courtesy of Murray Lee, Tennessee State Photo Services

Before the Manhattan Project forever altered the landscape of Oak Ridge, John Henry and Elizabeth Inman Welcker ran a plantation with over a dozen slaves along the Clinch River known as Laurel Banks. They arrived in the early 1800s and ran the plantation until their deaths in 1838 and 1840, respectively. Their slaves were buried in a cemetery that remains on the Department of Energy's property today. In May 2000, the site was renamed the Wheat Community African Burial Ground.

Beginning in early 1943, recruiters for the Manhattan Project sought African American workers throughout the South. Work on the project offered an escape from the Depression and the devastating drought that wreaked havoc on rural farming communities in the South and elsewhere.

Many black men left their families to work in Oak Ridge. They were provided with transportation to East Tennessee and offered an hourly

Men bring in coal
Photo courtesy of Ed Westcott

48

Scarboro School Girls' Basketball Team
Photo courtesy of Ed Westcott

wage of fifty-eight cents or more as laborers, janitors and domestic workers during the project. While they did not have the best jobs, their contribution to the success of the project was important.

For almost all the recruits, the pay and living conditions were considerably better than what they left behind. Except for the worksite, segregation remained the order of the day. African American workers ate in separate cafeterias, had separate recreational facilities, used different bathrooms and drinking fountains, sat in the back of the bus and experienced other indignities that were common practice at the time.

The army originally planned to construct a "Negro Village" for Oak Ridge's black workforce but had to abandon its plans as the demands for housing grew exponentially. Instead, many lived in sixteen-by-sixteen foot hutments. Early on, married black couples could not live together. Women lived in the "pen," an area with a ten o'clock curfew and guards stationed outside, purportedly for the women's safety.

Conditions were far from ideal. But most of the black workers were glad to have a job making some money and creating brighter prospects for the future.

Photo courtesy of Ed Westcott

DOCUMENTING OAK RIDGE

James Edward Westcott was one of the first fifty residents of Oak Ridge and the only person permitted to photograph the secret city during the war. He was twenty years old and largely self-taught as a photographer.

Westcott was transferred from Nashville to Knoxville in December 1942. He was an employee of the U.S. Army Corps of Engineers, but the reason for his selection for this important task is unclear. It may have been his proximity to the secret city, or his experience as a photographer, which was substantial for his age. It may also have been his youthfulness and enthusiasm that attracted the attention of the Manhattan Project leaders, who were more likely seeking competency and excellence for this task. Westcott fell in love with photography at a young age and began his own film developing business at age thirteen.

Whatever the reason for his recruitment, Westcott excelled as Oak Ridge's sole photographer. His beautiful and iconic images vividly depict life at Oak Ridge during the war.

OAK RIDGE COMMUNITY

Old Wildcat Den
MIDTOWN COMMUNITY CENTER

Youth Socialize at Old Wildcat Den
Photo courtesy of Ed Westcott

The "Old Wildcat Den" or the Midtown Community Center was the chief site for socializing at Oak Ridge *(pictured above)*. You could meet up with friends and listen to the jukebox or participate in dances or bowling tournaments.

For a community of its size, there were an extraordinary number of cultural activities. The Secret City boasted seven large theaters and performance spaces with a full schedule of plays, musicals, orchestras and swing bands. In good weather, regular outdoor dances were held on the tennis courts below the Guest House. With the average age of 27, it was a very youthful population.

AUSTRIAN FOLK DANCING
"I was born in Austria, spoke no English when I got here in 1938. I liked to folk dance and at Oak Ridge a Cornell professor taught international folk dances...When I saw the physical education teacher dance, well, I decided that she was going to be my wife! First time I told her I was going to marry her, she laughed! But I was very persistent. We had lots of fun!"

~Jack Shacter, AHF oral history, June 17, 2006

Alexander Guest House
FORMERLY THE ALEXANDER INN

The Alexander Guest House today
Photo courtesy of John Huotari/Oak Ridge Today

When General Leslie R. Groves came on one of his frequent visits to Oak Ridge, he usually stayed at the Guest House. Groves had a special suite reserved for him throughout the duration of the war.

The Guest House is a wood-framed building, constructed in 1943. In addition to General Groves, key Manhattan Project figures including Secretary of War Henry Stimson, Enrico Fermi, J. Robert Oppenheimer, James B. Conant and Vannevar Bush stayed here on their trips to Oak Ridge.

The name of the hotel was changed to the Alexander Inn in September 1950, a year after a 44-room addition was completed. The Inn's bar and restaurant were a social center for Oak Ridgers for decades. However, it was closed in the mid-1990s and fell into disrepair. Thanks to the efforts of local preservationists, the inn was restored as the Alexander Guest House, a senior assisted living facility in October 2015.

Visitors are welcome in the beautifully restored lobby. One can imagine Secretary Stimson exclaiming after his first tour of the plants that "Oak Ridge is the largest, most extraordinary scientific experiment in history!"

Chapel-on-the-Hill

The U.S. Army Corps of Engineers built the Chapel-on-the-Hill to accommodate the growing demands of Oak Ridgers for a place of worship. The pastor of Knoxville's First Baptist Church dedicated it on September 30, 1943. The pastor referred to it as the "Chapel-on-the-Hill" in a prayer and the name stuck. It has a standard U.S. Army Corps of Engineers building design known as a "700 Series" chapel.

During the war, twenty-two distinct religious organizations shared the Chapel. These included Catholic, Jewish, and Protestant congregations. Other services were held in local theaters. In 1955, the nondenominational United Church purchased the chapel and continues to perform services there to this day.

The chapel was a common place for wedding ceremonies for Oak Ridgers during the Manhattan Project. Despite its popularity, after the war the chapel faced a crisis when Tennessee Eastman employees, who comprised 40 percent of the worshipers, were terminated. However, the church was preserved because of Reverend B.M. Larson's leadership.

Today, the Chapel retains its ecumenical feel and has activities throughout the year. Its historic significance was recognized in 1993 when it was added to the National Register of Historic Places.

The Chapel in March 2004
Photo courtesy of D. Ray Smith

Jackson Square

Jackson Square
Photo courtesy of Oak Ridge Convention and Visitors' Bureau

Jackson Square was the heart of Oak Ridge's business district. Originally Town Center No. 1, the name Jackson Square was adopted in February 1945 as Oak Ridge moved away from military terminology. The site was one of five commercial shopping areas distributed across the Oak Ridge reservation.

Residents frequented the square on weekends and weekdays to shop at stores including Miller's Department Store, Hall's Shoes, Hamilton Bank, Sutton's barbershop, and the Arcade. In addition, Jackson Square was the heart of music production and theater in Oak Ridge. The Oak Ridge Symphony, the Oak Ridge Chorus, and the Concert Band soon began giving regular performances in the Ridge Recreation Hall. The Center Theatre served as the community playhouse.

On August 14, 1945, Jackson Square was where residents celebrated the end of World War II waving the banner headlines "WAR ENDS. "

JACKSON SQUARE KNOT
"In 1944, Robert 'Red' and Helen (Davis) Lynch met working in Miller's Department Store at Jackson Square but spent time together at the skating rink, bowling or the movies. Red was captain of the Monsanto Roller Hockey Team and played basketball for Trico Motors. In September 2011, the Lynches celebrated their 65th anniversary."

~Barbara Ann "Bobbie" Martin (daughter), September 16, 2011

Manhattan Project Park

The Manhattan Project National Historical Park was over a decade in the making. In 2004, Congress directed the National Park Service (NPS) to study whether there should be a Manhattan Project park. Ten years later, Congress passed and President Obama signed legislation creating the park at Oak Ridge, TN, Los Alamos, NM and Hanford, WA.

On November 10, 2015, the Secretaries of Energy and Interior signed a Memorandum of Agreement that officially establishes the park and defines the responsibilities of each agency. As the nation's storyteller, the National Park Service will interpret the Manhattan Project. The Department of Energy will preserve its Manhattan Project properties and provide for public access and safety.

AMERICA'S STORYTELLER
"The National Park Service will be proud to interpret these Manhattan Project sites and unlock their stories in the years ahead."
~Jonathan Jarvis, Director of the National Park Service, 2011

The new Manhattan Project Park will be the first to recognize one of the most significant undertakings in modern history that introduced atomic energy to mankind. It will also be one of the few parks that focuses on American science, technology, and industry. The park offers a great opportunity to engage young people in learning about innovations and how science and technology can shape the future.

The new park will offer stories with diverse, multicultural perspectives, recognizing the role of immigrants, women and minorities at Oak Ridge. The park will also embrace difficult issues concerning the decision to use the atomic bombs, their impact on the Japanese, and legacy for today. The interpretation will encourage visitors to place themselves in the context of World War II and reflect upon this history from different perspectives.

Here are some of the historic Manhattan Project properties in Oak Ridge that may be available to the public as part of the new park. Be sure to start with the American Museum of Science and Energy for an overview of the history and information about public access and tours.

The K-25 plant site. Although the plant was demolished, the mile-long footprint was preserved. The Department of Energy has plans to create an interpretive center with an observation tower at the site.

The X-10 Graphite Reactor. This pilot-scale reactor was built after the Chicago Pile-I in just 10 months. It served as a model for the reactors at Hanford.

Beta-3 Calutrons (Building 9204-3 at the Y-12 plant) separated the isotopes of uranium for the Little Boy bomb and continued to be used for isotope separation for over 50 years.

The X-10 Graphite Reactor

Pilot Plant (Building 9731 at the Y-12 plant) demonstrated isotope separation techniques.

Alexander Guest House was recently renovated as a senior assisted living center, restoring the lobby as it was in the 1940s. Other nearby sites include the Chapel-on-the-Hill, Jackson Square and thousands of "alphabet" houses. Enjoy!

WHY WE REMEMBER
"The new weapon was built in makeshift buildings, laboratories and factories all over the United States. Now nearly 70 years later, some of these historic places of the Manhattan Project will at last be preserved as part of the national historical park. The Manhattan Project is significant not only for its role in ending World War II but for introducing a major new force in human affairs. Reason enough to be remembered."

~*Richard Rhodes*, author of The Making of the Atomic Bomb, *2014*

Veterans Remember

Manhattan Project veterans Robert J. Vogel, William E. Tewes, William G. Palmer and Lawrence S. O'Rourke on Bear Mountain, NY

MUM'S THE WORD

"Bill Tewes went his way every day on a bus to K-25, as did I, but I never knew where he went once inside the gate of K-25. I had no idea what Bill was doing, nor would he say, nor would I say, nor would anybody I ever knew say. We were very, very close. Our Special Engineer Detachment kept their mouths shut. To this day, I still don't know what Bill did. As close as we are, to this day—it's inured into us."

~Lawrence S. O'Rourke, AHF oral history, March 2013

ATOMIC SCIENCE JOLTS PUBLIC

"After the Hiroshima and Nagasaki bombs were dropped and the war was over, it's very hard to reconstruct the feeling that existed in this country about atomic work. People talked about atoms as if that was something totally new and totally unexpected, mysterious and secret. You talked to a person on the street about atoms, and they were all a-tither. It's very hard to reconstruct the intense feeling people had about atomic science."

~Dieter Gruen, AHF oral history, February 2015

Chronology
THE MAKING OF THE ATOMIC BOMB

1899 New Zealand physicist Ernest Rutherford identifies two kinds of natural radiation: alpha particles and beta rays.

1905 Albert Einstein proposes a theory, shown most dramatically in a nuclear explosion, that defines the relationship between energy and mass: $E=mc^2$.

1932 British physicist James Chadwick discovers the neutron.

1933 Hungarian physicist Leo Szilard first conceives of a nuclear chain reaction and the potential for an atomic bomb.

1934 Italian physicist Enrico Fermi and his team in Rome bombard elements with neutrons and split uranium but do not realize it.

1938 Otto Hahn and Fritz Strassmann, German physicists, discover the fission process by splitting uranium in two. Austrian physicists Lise Meitner and Otto Frisch coin the term "nuclear fission" and publish results.

1939 Danish physicist Niels Bohr announces recent discoveries about fission by European colleagues at an international conference on theoretical physics in Washington, DC.

Aug. 2, 1939 Einstein sends a letter to President Franklin D. Roosevelt warning of the prospect of Germany developing an atomic bomb.

Sept. 1, 1939 Nazi Germany invades Poland; World War II begins.

June 1940 The National Defense Research Committee (NDRC) is established to organize U.S. scientific resources for war, including research on the atom and the fission of uranium.

Feb. 24, 1941 American scientist Glenn T. Seaborg's research team discovers plutonium.

June 22, 1941 Nazi Germany invades the Soviet Union.

Oct. 9, 1941	President Roosevelt asks the Chairman of the NDRC, Vannevar Bush, to determine the cost of an atomic bomb and explore construction needs with the Army.
Dec. 7, 1941	Japan attacks Pearl Harbor.
Dec. 8, 1941	The United States Congress declares war on Japan.
Dec. 11, 1941	Germany and Italy declare war on the United States.
Jan. 19, 1942	President Roosevelt approves the production of an atomic bomb.
Aug.13, 1942	General order is issued by the Chief of Engineers formally establishing the Manhattan Engineer District (MED) for construction of an atomic bomb.
Sept. 17, 1942	Colonel Leslie R. Groves takes over command of the MED.
Sept. 19, 1942	Groves selects Oak Ridge, TN, as the site for a pilot plant for uranium isotope separation.
Nov. 25, 1942	Groves selects Los Alamos, NM, as the scientific research laboratory, codenamed "Project Y." J. Robert Oppenheimer is chosen as laboratory director.
Dec. 2, 1942	Fermi's team produces the first sustained nuclear fission chain reaction under the bleachers at University of Chicago's Stagg Field.
Jan. 16, 1943	Groves selects Hanford, WA, as a site for plutonium production.
July 17, 1944	Major reorganization to maximize plutonium implosion research occurs at Los Alamos after the plutonium gun-type bomb is abandoned.
April 12, 1945	Franklin D. Roosevelt dies and Harry S. Truman becomes President.
April 25, 1945	Groves and Secretary of War Henry Stimson brief Truman on the Manhattan Project.
May 7, 1945	Nazi Germany surrenders to the Allies.

June 6, 1945	Stimson and other members of the Interim Committee recommend to President Truman that the atomic bomb be used as soon as possible without warning.
June 1945	The Franck Report, urging demonstration of the bomb before military use, begins circulating among scientists.
July 16, 1945	Trinity test, the first nuclear explosion, is successfully conducted in Alamogordo, NM.
July 17, 1945	Potsdam Conference of President Truman, Prime Minister Winston Churchill and Communist Party General Secretary Joseph Stalin begins.
July 21, 1945	Truman approves order for the use of atomic bombs.
July 24, 1945	Truman informs Stalin that the United States has developed a powerful new weapon.
July 26, 1945	Potsdam Declaration asks Japan for unconditional surrender and warns of "prompt and utter destruction."
July 29, 1945	Japan rejects the Potsdam Declaration.
Aug. 6, 1945	The Little Boy uranium bomb is dropped on Hiroshima, Japan.
Aug. 9, 1945	The Fat Man plutonium bomb is dropped on Nagasaki, Japan.
Aug. 14, 1945	Japan surrenders.
Jan. 24, 1946	The United Nations adopts its first resolution, which establishes the United Nations Atomic Energy Commission.
May 21, 1946	Louis Slotin receives a lethal dose of radiation conducting an experiment at Los Alamos. He dies on May 30, 1946.
Aug. 1, 1946	President Truman establishes the Atomic Energy Commission (AEC), which assumes responsibility for all property in the custody and control of the MED.
Aug. 15, 1947	The Manhattan Engineer District is abolished.

Sources
AND FURTHER READING

MANHATTAN PROJECT HISTORY

Atomic Heritage Foundation websites: www.AtomicHeritage.org and www.ManhattanProjectVoices.org.

Bird, Kai and Martin J. Sherwin. *American Prometheus: The Triumph and Tragedy of J. Robert Oppenheimer.* New York: Knopf, 2005.

Groueff, Stephane, *Manhattan Project: The Untold Story of the Making of the Atomic Bomb.* Boston: Little, Brown, 1967.

Groves, Leslie R. *Now It Can Be Told: The Story of the Manhattan Project.* New York: Harper, 1962.

Hasegawa, Tsuyoshi. *Racing the Enemy: Stalin, Truman and the Surrender of Japan.* Cambridge, MA: Harvard University Press, 2005.

Kelly, Cynthia C., ed. *The Manhattan Project: The Birth of the Atomic Bomb in the Words of Its Creators, Eyewitnesses and Historians.* New York: Black Dog & Leventhal, 2007.

Norris, Robert S. *Racing for the Bomb: General Leslie R. Groves, the Manhattan Project's Indispensable Man.* Vermont: Steerforth Press, 2002.

Rhodes, Richard. *The Making of the Atomic Bomb.* New York: Simon & Schuster, 1986.

OAK RIDGE HISTORY

'43 Club Cookbook Committee. *Cooking Behind the Fence: Recipes and Recollections from the Oak Ridge '43 Club.* Oak Ridge: Oak Ridge Heritage & Preservation Association.

Gailar, Joanne Stern. *Oak Ridge and Me: From Youth to Maturity.* Oak Ridge: Children's Museum of Oak Ridge, 1991.

Hogerton, John F. "Largest of the Atom-Bomb Plants." *Engineering News-Record*, December 13, 1945.

Hooper, Ed. *Knoxville in World War II.* Charleston: Arcardia, 2006.

Johnson, Charles W. and Charles O. Jackson. *City Behind A Fence: Oak Ridge, Tennessee, 1942-1946.* Knoxville: University of Tennessee Press, 1981.

Johnson, Leland and Daniel Schaffer. *Oak Ridge National Laboratory: The First Fifty Years.* Knoxville: University of TN Press, 1994.

Kiernan, Denise. *The Girls of Atomic City: The Untold Story of the Women Who Helped Win World War II.* New York: Touchstone, 2013.

Overholt, James, ed. *These Are Our Voices: The Story of Oak Ridge, 1942-1970.* Oak Ridge: Children's Museum of Oak Ridge, 1987.

Rockwell, Theodore. *Creating the New World: Stories & Images from the Dawn of the Atomic Age.* Bloomington: 1st Books Library, 2003.

Smith, David Ray. *John Hendrix Story.* Oak Ridge: Lulu, 2010.

Smithsonian Videohistory Program. Manhattan Project Interviews, Collection Division 2: Oak Ridge, 4 Sessions. 9531. Stanley Goldberg, Interviewer. March 3-6, 1987.

Smyser, Dick. *Oak Ridge 1942-1992: A Commemorative Portrait.* Oak Ridge: Oak Ridge Community Foundation, 1992.

Trauger, Donald B. *Horse Power to Nuclear Power: Memoir of an Energy Pioneer.* Franklin: Hillsboro Press, 2002.

U.S. Department of Energy/Martin Marietta Energy Systems, Inc. *Oak Ridge National Laboratory Review.* Vol 25, Nos. 3 and 4. 1992.

Weinberg, Alvin M. *The First Nuclear Era: The Life and Times of a Technological Fixer.* New York: American Institute of Physics, 1994.

Westcott, Ed. *Images of America: Oak Ridge,* Charleston: Arcadia, 2005.

Wilcox, Wm. J. Jr., *A Brief History of K-25,* The Secret City Store, Oak Ridge, Tennessee, 2006.

Wilcox, Wm. J. Jr. *An Overview of the History of Y-12, 1942-1992,* The Secret City Store, Oak Ridge, 2009.

Yates, Sam, ed. *Through the Lens of Ed Westcott: A Photographic History of World War II's Secret City.* Oak Ridge: University of TN Press, 2005.

Places to See

IN OAK RIDGE

AMERICAN MUSEUM OF SCIENCE AND ENERGY
300 South Tulane Avenue
(865) 576-3200
www.amse.org

CHILDREN'S MUSEUM OF OAK RIDGE
461 West Outer Drive
(865) 482-1074
http://childrensmuseumo-foakridge.org/

EAST TENNESSEE TECHNOLOGY PARK OVERLOOK
251 Highway 58
(865) 574-9683

NEW HOPE CENTER'S Y-12 HISTORY CENTER
602 Scarboro Road
(865) 574-3280
http://www.y12.doe.gov/about/

SECRET CITY COMMEMORATIVE WALK
1403 Oak Ridge Turnpike
(865) 482-7821

HISTORIC JACKSON SQUARE
East Tennessee Avenue
(865) 482-8450

SECRET CITY SCENIC TRAIN
Hwy. 58, East Tennessee Technology Park
(865) 241-2140
www.secretcityrailroad.com/

WHEAT COMMUNITY AFRICAN BURIAL GROUND
Hwy. 58, adjacent to East Tennessee Technology Park Overlook

OTHER SITES

GREEN McADOO CULTURAL CENTER
101 School Street, Clinton
(865) 463-6500
www.greenmcadoo.org

COAL MINERS MUSEUM
201 South Main Street, Lake City
(865) 457-4547
coalcreekminersmuseum.com

GREAT SMOKY MOUNTAINS NATIONAL PARK
107 Park Headquarters Road, Gatlinburg
(865) 436-1200
www.nps.gov/grsm

MUSEUM OF APPALACHIA
2819 Andersonville Hwy, Clinton
(865) 494-7680
www.museumofappalachia.org

NORRIS DAM STATE PARK
125 Village Green Circle, Rocky Top
(865) 426-7461
www.norrislakeinfo.com

UT McCLUNG MUSEUM
1327 Circle Park Drive, Knoxville
(865) 974-2144
http://mcclungmuseum.utk.edu/